This book is a testament of how far our boys have progressed. In two short years, our students have learned how to read and have evolved into budding authors. The priceless tool of written communication will serve them well throughout their lives.

Thank you to Kids Write Network for providing our boys with such a wonderful opportunity. Thank you to our amazing, talented and dedicated teachers Linda Mahler and Alti Neuwirth for working closely with the boys and enriching their lives.

Table of Contents:

Passport

Name: Sholem, NeuwiRth

Date of Birth: November 10 2009

Birthplace: MontRéal Canada

Issue date: June 5 2017

I'd like to travel to....

China and North Korea

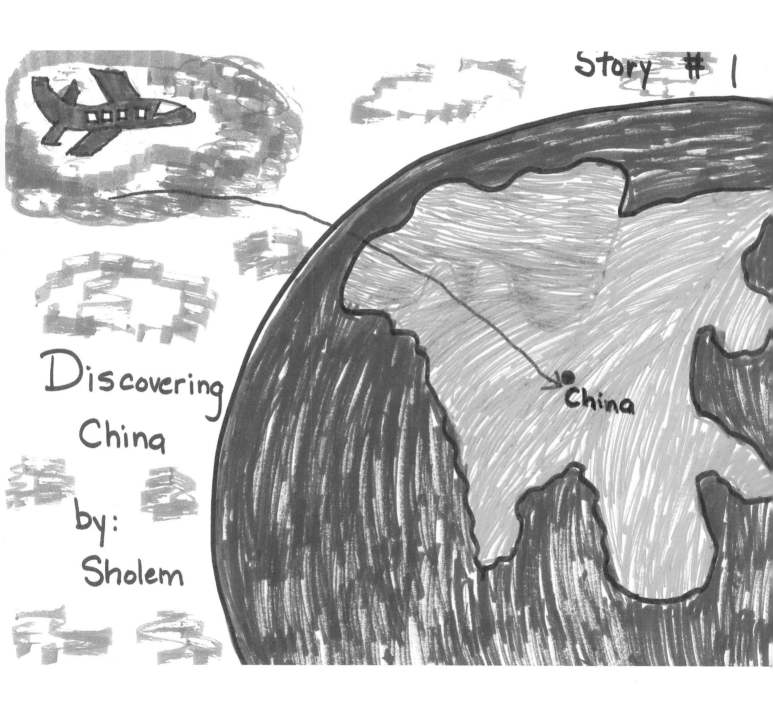

Story # 1

Discovering
China

by:
Sholem

China

Sholem

I would like to go see the great wall of china. I would like to see
some interesting chinese animals. I would also like to see
some towers like the shanghai tower.

I would eat chinese food. I would go to the markets to buy things because it's very cheap. I would buy fidget spinners for my whole class. Everyone will be so happy.

I would learn that eventhough some things are cheap, they are not always worth it. They can break easily. I would learn the chinese language and the art of kongfu. I would also learn how to cook some chinese dishes.

I would feel great about going to China and would want to go back again.
After going to China I would want to go to North Koria to see the
evil guy in charge of that country.

Passport

Name: israel Wasserman

Date of Birth: March 11 2009

Birthplace: Montreal canada

Issue date: June 5 2017

I'd like to travel to....
Niagara Falls

North America

Niagra Falls

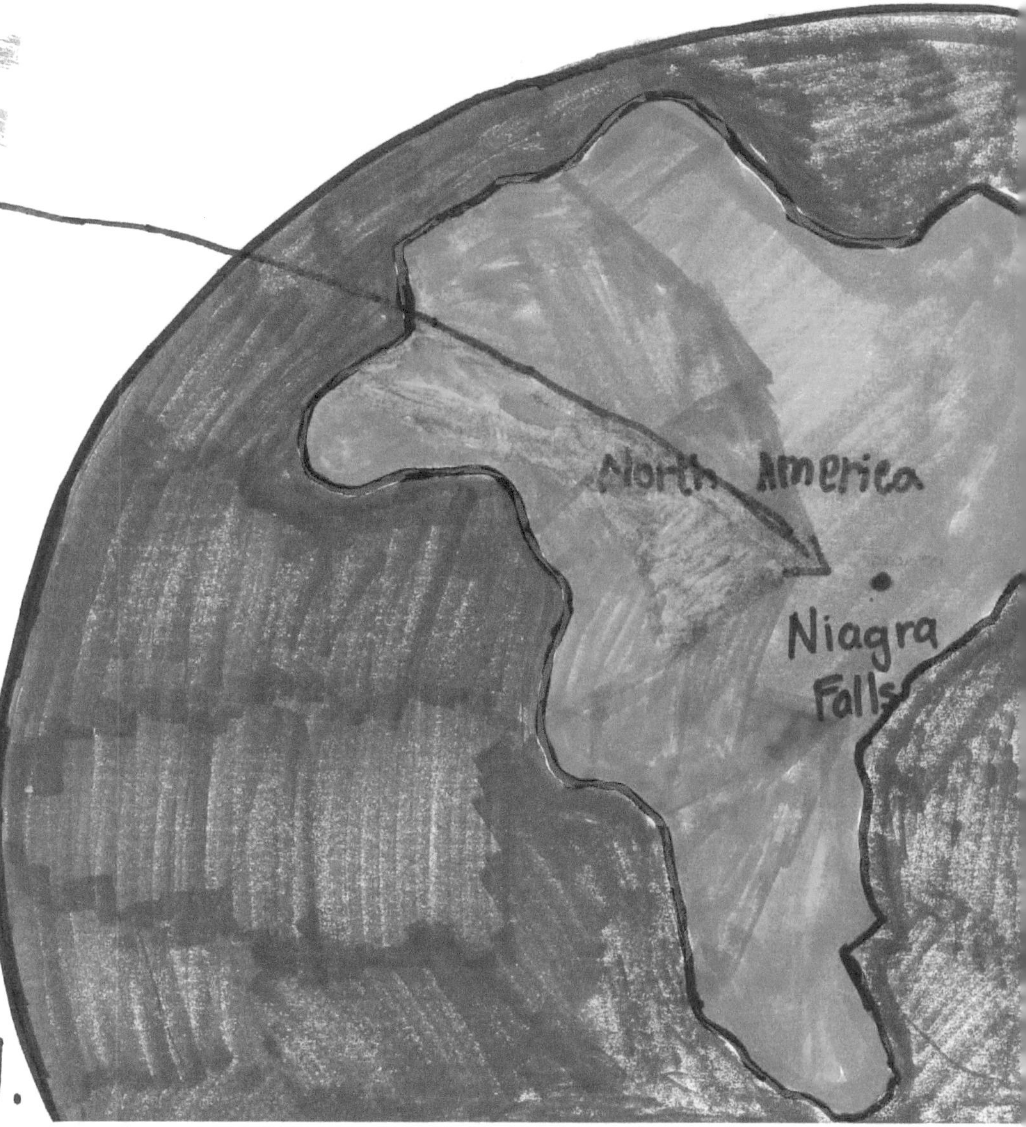

Having Fun
in
Niagra Falls
by
Yisroel W.

yisroel

I want to see the beautiful water Falls go over the cliff because they are very beaubiful. I also want to see the colorful Rainbow in the sky. I would also have a great time on the boat with my family

I would go on All the water slides with my brother in the Hotel And out the Hotel. I would also go swiming. I would Love to Hang out with my family because I love them.

I WOULD leaRn about i travelling to a new place so
tact i could learn about new places. by going to visit
niagra Falls, I WOULD now that there are Further
places than Montreal.

I woUlD feel Happy to Have baD gone on this
fun trip but I WoUlD be saD to leave. but i
would feel Happy again wehe i get Home.
Home swete Home

Photo

Passport

Name: YITZY

Date of Birth: NOV 9TH 2018

Birthplace: MONTREAL

Issue date: JUNE 5TH 2017

I'd like to travel to....

ISREAL AND PRINCE EDWARD ISLAND

www.sunshineandteaching.com

LIVING IN ISRAEL   Story #3   by: Yitzy

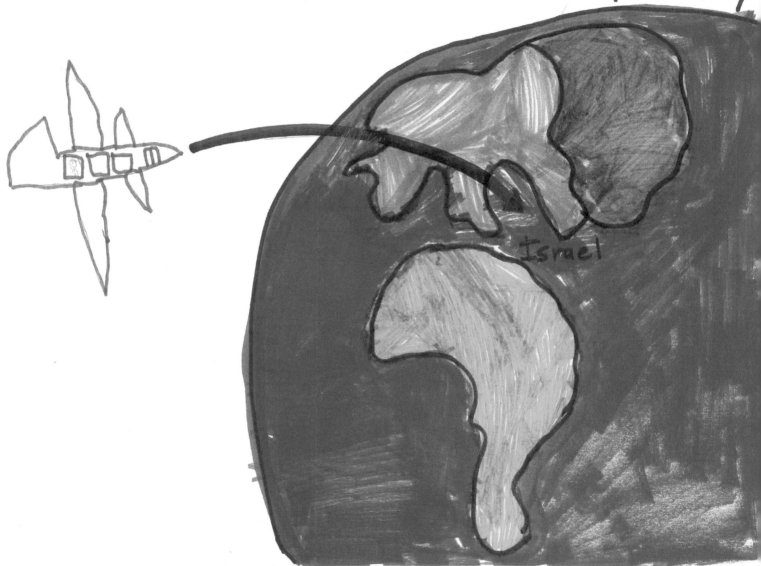

THIS IS THE WESTERN WALL.
I WOULD GO SEE THE ISRALI ARMY I WOULD GO SEE
THE KOTEL IN THE WESTERN PART OF ISRAEL. I WOULD GO TO SEE
MERON TO SEE WHERE RABBI SHIMON BAR YOCHAI IS
BURIED.

I WOULD WANT TO GO OUT TO RESTAURANTS
I WOULD GO VISIT MY SISTER. I WOULD FEELL HAPPY TO
SEE MY SISTER, CHAVA WHO WAS A COMBAT MEDIC IN THE
ISRALI ARMY.

I WOULD LEARN THER LANGUAGE
WHICH IS HEBREW

I WOULD FEEL HAPPY TO GO TO ISRAEL
BECAUE I'VE NEVER BEEN THERE BEFORE

Photo

Passport

Name: Yosef

Date of Birth: ᓂᑌᑎᒎ ᕒ

Birthplace: Montreal, Canada

Issue date: June 5

I'd like to travel to.... Florida

I like visiting the city of Florida

by: Yosef

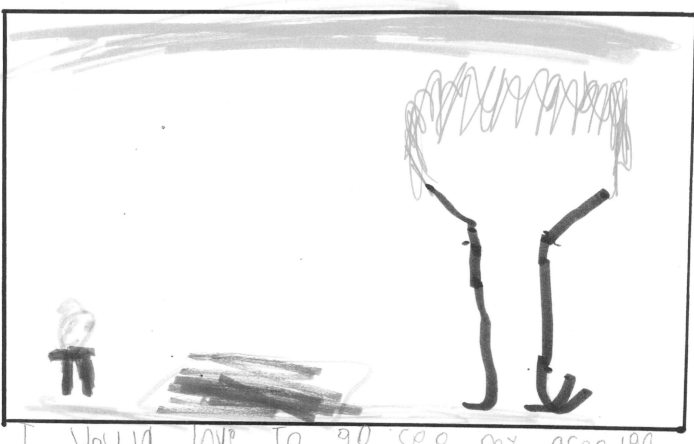

I would love to go see my grandpa and my friends. I would go for a walk to see all the beautiful trees and flowers.

I would go swimming. I would go to the PACK. I would also play in the sand. I would love to rent a cool car to drive through.

yosef

I would learn to swim better than I already do. I would learn all about air planes because they are interesting

I would feel happy to see the people I've missed. I would feel glad to relax. I would feel happy thay I went to the ice cream shop in florida.

 # Passport

Name: Sruli Marstek

Date of Birth: כ' בכסלו

Birthplace: Montreal Canada

Issue date: June 5 2017

 I'd like to travel to....

antartica

www.sunshineandteaching.com

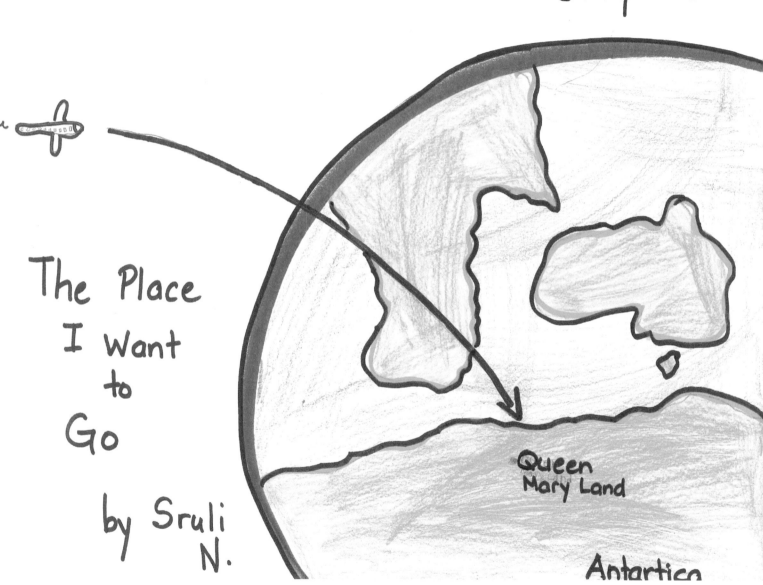

The Place
I Want
to
Go

by Sruli
N.

Queen
Mary Land

Antartica

Sruli

I Would see Many penguins. I Would see
Polar bears. I Would see a lot of Snow. I would
see A Frozen Lake That I can go Iceskating on.

I Would Play with The Penguins. I Would Build an igloo.
I Would also feed The Polar bears With fish from The
Lake. I Would play Tackle Football With The Penguins.

I Would Learn That It,S A very cold Place. I Would Learn How to Interact with The penguins and Polar bears. I Would Also Learn How To go Iceskating with the Penguins and Polar bears.

I would feel sad because I would miss the penguins and polar bears. I would Feel Happy That I Went.

Passport

Name: MOISh ZAVEL LISon

Date of Birth: ה׳ שנה

Birthplace: MONTREAL CANADA

Issue date: JUNe 5 5775

I'd like to travel to....

FLORIDA

www.sunshineandteaching.com

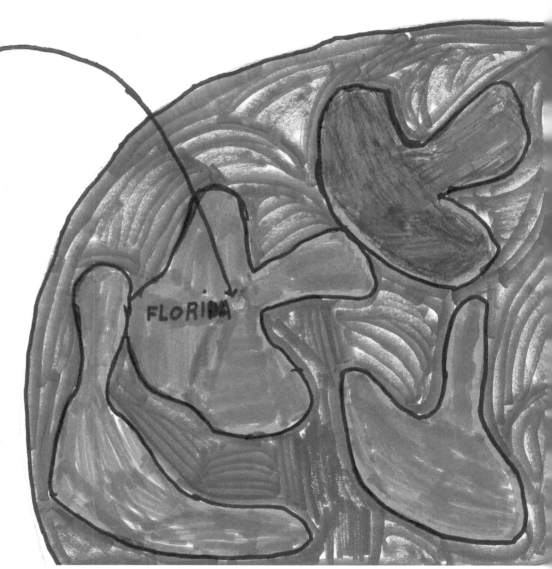

FLORIDA

Enjoying
Florida

by:
Moish

Moish

I would like to see people on gliding boats.
I would love to see whales. I would
also love to see my cousins.

Moish

I CAN TRY TO bVild boats

I CAN CATCH LiZARdS AND fish.

I WOULD Like TOTAN ONtHe BEACH.

I WOULD LEARN that THERE aRE
PLaces IN the WORld that can be
LoTs OF FuN.

I WOULD FEEL SAD because I wish I can stay there FOREVER. I WOULD FEEL so hAPPY THAT I WENT TO FLORIDA.

VISITOR - Permitted to remain

Passport

Name: David Menachem

Date of Birth: June 6,

Birthplace: Mexico

Issue date: May 2, 2017

I'd like to travel to....
New York

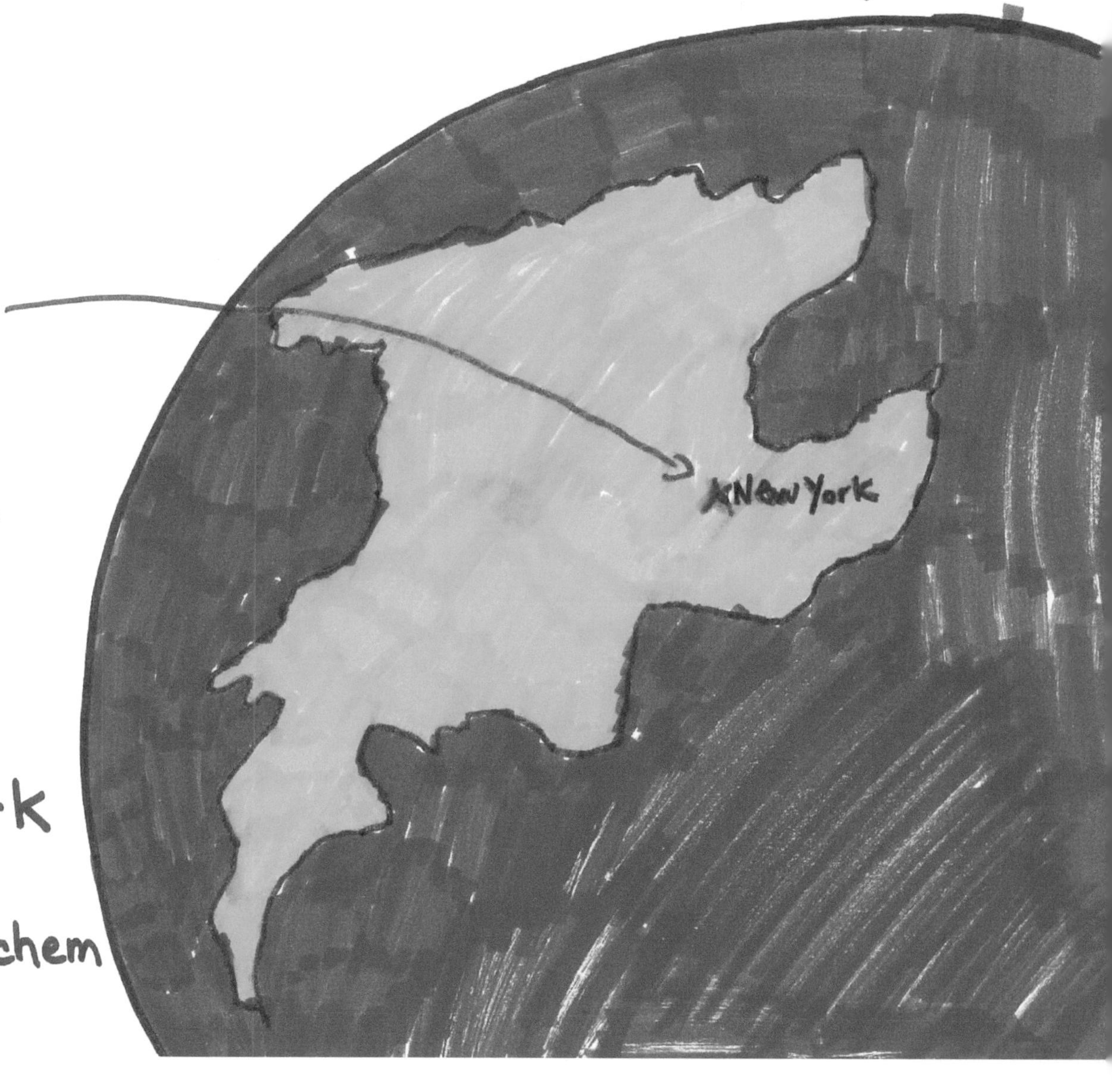

My first
time
in
New York

David Menachem

New York

I would like To go see my aunT. I would like To see The StaTue oF Liberty. I WOuld WanT TO see hoW bid iT is.

I would want to go to the
Empire state building.
I would want to go to
the toy store.

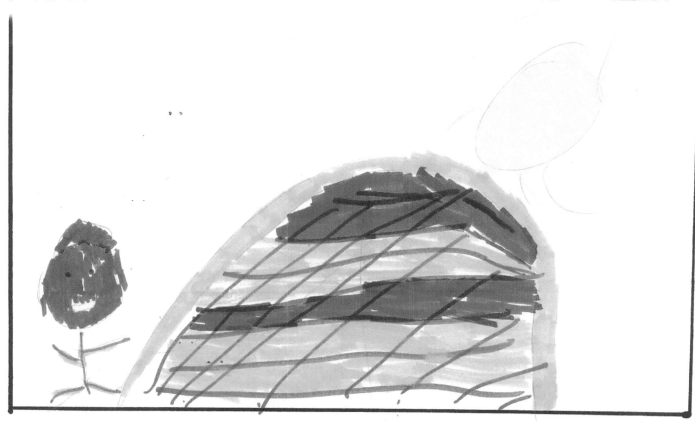

I learnt That there are many brdges in New york.
I learnt Thare are many boic dings to see.
I would learn That new york is a big city.

David. M

I would feel Happy after my trip to New york
because I saw many new things.
I would feel sad to go home. because I had a lot of
fun in New york

Passport

Photo

Name: ELI

Date of Birth: first day of PASACH

Birthplace: MONtreAl

Issue date: MAY 18, 2017

I'd like to travel to.... HaWAii

www.sunshineandteaching.com

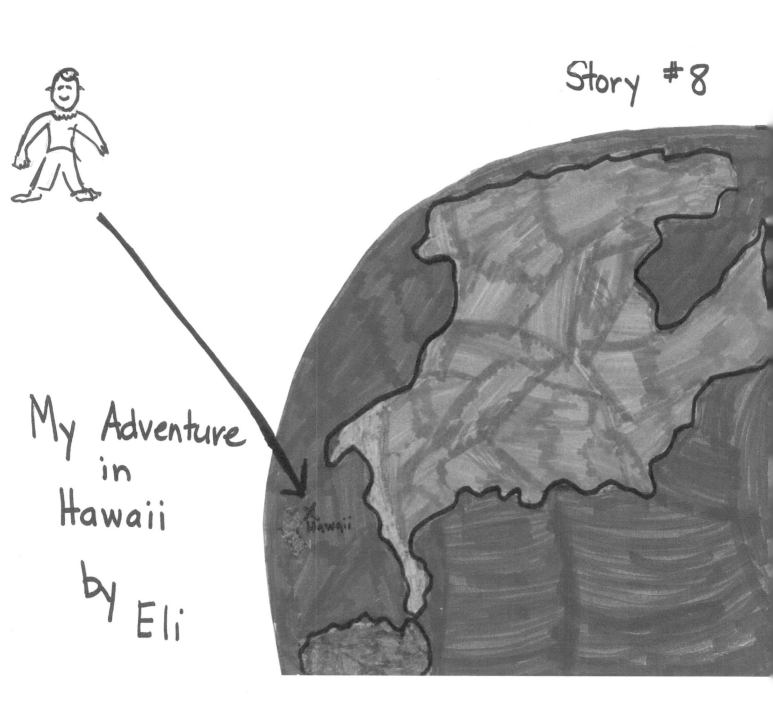

My Adventure
in
Hawaii

by Eli

Eli

1)I wou see the Ocean 2)I would like to go see the volcanos
I would want to see RED lava which is liquid Rock. I would get dehydrated. But there is an ocean for swiming And cool off

I vould go swimming AmI vould plag in the SAND
MAKE ASANd RAStle Then Belly flop on it ANd it will
sound like "poof" my mother will be laying on
A chair And my dad to. meanwhile my brothers are swiming

dange-
rous

CAref-
ul

I would learn that volcanos are dangerous and I would learn to be careful when I swim. Volcanos are dangros becaus there is lava inside and lava is so dangros. In hawii you also have to be careful when youl there because there is an ocean and you dont want to get eaten by a shark

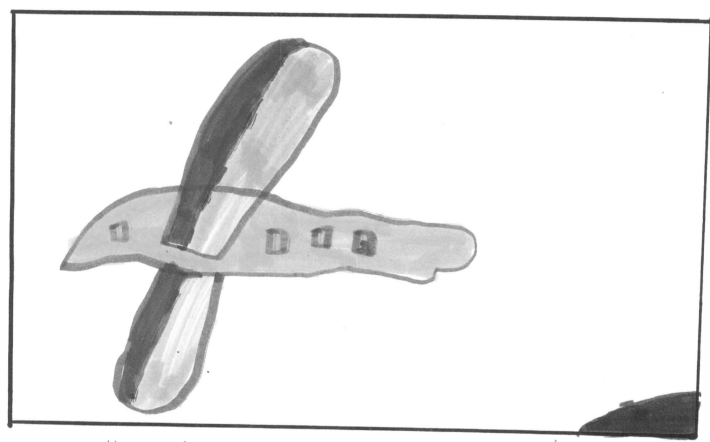

I would feel awesome after my trip because I got to go to the beach in middle of Montreal's winter. And I would feel sad because I have to leave.

Milton Keynes UK
Ingram Content Group UK Ltd.
UKHW050923050124
435446UK00003B/10

9 781941 664001